Beginning Reading Instruction

LEVEL 1B

B
Piper
Books

D1359114

Instructions

Reader

- Say the sounds and read the word.
- When you know the word, just say it; there is no further need to say the sounds.
- No guessing! None! Read through the word.

Instructor

- Point out any letter/sound correspondences introduced in the new story.
- When the reader struggles with a word, tell them the correct sound(s) only after they have tried hard to remember.
- **Don't** try to provide any other help or explanation.
- Praise frequently, and end each session well before the reader becomes tired.

Story Discussion

- On completion of each story, if using the Questions encourage the learner to answer in full sentences and to reread the relevant page(s) if necessary.
- Many children will benefit from this increased scrutiny; others may benefit more from rereading or moving on to the next book.

See › www.piperbooks.co.uk › RESOURCES › BRI free resources for BRI Level 1 Initial and Mastery Assessments and a book-by-book Pupil Progress Sheet, including a record of word, sound and letter(s) introduction and a tutor comments column.

Contents

STORY 1

Meet Mit

Story Synopsis

One day Mit the Chimp discovers Sam the Lion taking a nap. Mit wants to introduce himself formally to Sam and tries to awaken him. When Sis the Snake comes along, they both try to rouse the Lion, but it is no use. Sam finally does wake up, but he is in a very grumpy mood – at least until he meets Sis.

New Words

meet

New Letter(s)/Sounds

(none)

Speech, Language and Communication

Factual Questions

Name three things Mit does when he's introducing people.

p13 Is Sam awake yet?

Developing Comprehension

p12 What do Sis and Mit do to Sam?

p16-17 Does Sam cheer up? Why?

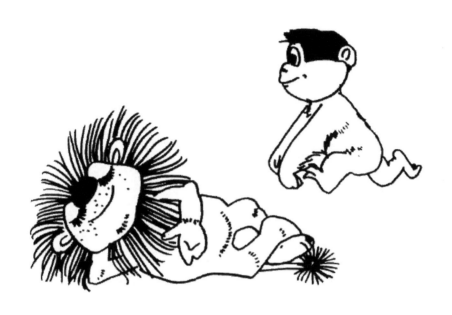

See Sam. See Mit.

"Meet me, Sam. I am Mit."

"Meet me, Sis. I am Mit."

"Sis, meet Sam."

"Sam, Sam! Meet Sis."

"Meet Sis, Sam."

See Mit. See Sis. See Sam.

See Sam.

"I am Sam! I am Sam!"

"Sam, Sam."

"Sam, meet Sis."

"Sis, meet Sam."

"See Sam? See Sis?"

"Meet me."

STORY 2

See It

Story Synopsis

Mat the Rat, Mit the Chimp and Sis the Snake are playing ball on a very hot day. Mercifully they spot some shade and collapse in it, only to discover when it wanders off that it's the shadow of Will the Elephant. The animals introduce themselves and go for a ride on Will's back.

New Words	New Letter(s)/Sounds
in	'n' /n/
it	(none)
sees*	's' /z/

The spelling 's' represents both the sound /s/ as in 'see' and /z/ as in 'sees'.

Speech, Language and Communication

Factual Questions

p23 What is the weather like?

p26-27 Where does Mat go?

Developing Comprehension

p24-25 Why do you think that Mat, Mit and Sis look unhappy?

p30 What is going to go wrong with the animals' lie-down?

"See me, Mit."

See Mat. See Mit. See Sis.

"See it, Mat.

See it, Sis."

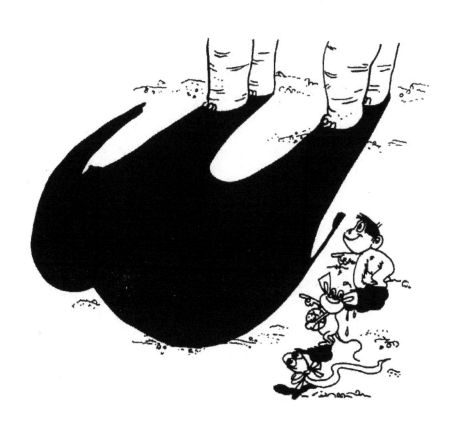

Mit sees it.

Mat sees it.

Sis sees it.

"See me in it, Sis.

See me in it, Mit."

"I am in it."

"I am in it."

See Mit in it.

See Mat in it.

See Sis in it.

"See it, Mat."

"I see it."

"See it! See it!"

"I see it."

"Meet me. I am Mat.

Meet Sis.

Meet Mit."

See Mit.

See Mit in it.

See Mat in it.

See Sis in it.

STORY 3

Sit on It

Story Synopsis

Mat the Rat is pulling a wagon when he meets first Mit the Chimp, then Sis the Snake, and then Sam the Lion. Each of Mat's friends wants a ride in the wagon. Mat gives Mit and Sis a ride. But when Sam tries to get in too, the wagon breaks, and Mat gets angry. Sam salvages a board from the wagon and carries the others to the beach on it. There they all play in the water on their new "surfboard".

New Words	New Letter(s)/Sounds
sit	(none)
on	'o' /o/

Speech, Language and Communication

Factual Questions

p43 Which animals are in the wagon?

p47 Can you remember what Sam uses this plank of wood for?

Developing Comprehension

p45 How do the other animals feel when Sam climbs into the wagon?

p46 Why do you think the wagon broke?

"See me."

"Meet me. Meet me.

I am Mit."

"See me.

I sit in it."

"I am Sis."

"I sit in it.

See me sit in it."

"See Mat.

See Mit sit in it.

See Sis sit in it."

"See me. See me sit in it."

"See! See!"

"See it."

"See it on Sam."

"See me on it."

See Sis on it.

See Mat on it.

See Sam on it.

STORY 4

Sis

Story Synopsis

Sis the Snake is asleep on a hollow log when Mit the Chimp awakens her. Mit has an apple which he teases Sis with. Then the chase begins. Over the log and through the hollow log they both go until Sis is tangled in a knot. Mit kindly untangles her and then they sit together sharing the apple.

New Words	New Letter(s)/Sounds
is	(none)

Speech, Language and Communication

Factual Questions

p57 Mit has something that Sis wants. What is it?

p58-59 How do you know that the log is hollow?

Developing Comprehension

p63 Is Sis *on top of* the log, *under* the log, or *inside* the log?

p65 Are Mit and Sis friends again? Why?

Sis sits on it.

Sis sees Mit.

Sis sees it.

Mit is in it.

Sis is in it.

Mit is on it.

"I see Sis in it."

"Mit! Mit!"

Mit sits.

Mit sees Sis.

Mit is on it.

Sis is in it.

Mit sits on it.

Sis sits on it.

STORY 5

Sam Sat

Story Synopsis

Mat the Rat has finished making a canoe and wants to try it out.
Sam the Lion wants to try it out too, but when he sits in the canoe
it tips over. Mat and Sam fight over the canoe, and they both end
up in the water. Mat and Sam finally solve the problem by having
Mat sit on Sam's head.

New Words	**New Letter(s)/Sounds**
sat	(none)

Speech, Language and Communication

Factual Questions

p69 What is Mat building?

p76 What happens to Sam?

Developing Comprehension

p78 Why is Mat trying to push Sam out of the canoe?

p80-82 How do Sam and Mat become friends again?

"I sit in it."

"Sit in it, Mat!
Sit in it."

"I sat in it."

"I see it on Mat."

Mat sat in it.

"See me sit in it."

Sam sat in it.

"Sam!"

See Mat. See Sam.

"I sit in it."

Mat sat in it.

Sam sat in it.

"I am Sam. I sit in it.

Sit on me, Mat."

Sam sat in it.

Mat sat on Sam.

Mat on Sam.

STORY 6

It is Ann

Story Synopsis

Mat the Rat introduces Ann the Giraffe to the rest of the animals. Ann has a hat, and they all think it would be fun for Sis the Snake to sit in it. When she does, the hat falls and lands on Mat. With the hat over his eyes, Mat tries to guess who is standing next to him. To his embarrassment, Mat finally has to be told that it is Ann.

New Words	New Letter(s)/Sounds
Ann	'nn' /n/*
this	'th' /th/

The sound /n/ has the spelling alternative 'nn'.

Speech, Language and Communication

Factual Questions

p92 What happens to Mat?

p98 Who is sulking?

Developing Comprehension

p89 What do the other animals want Sis to do?

p96-97 Why doesn't Mat understand that this is Ann?

"I am Ann. Meet me."

"Mit, this is Ann. Meet Ann."

"Sam, this is Ann."

"This is Ann, Sis."

"See it. Sit in it, Sis."

"Sis is in it.

See Sis sit in it."

"Ann, see it!"

"Mat is in it!"

It is on Mat.

"I am Mat.

This is on me."

"Is this Mit?"

"Is this Sis?"

"Is it Sam?"

"It is Ann!

It is Ann!"

Stories in
BRI: Beginning Reading Instruction Programme:

This edition of BRI (Beginning Reading Instruction) Level 1B
Published in 2020 by Piper Books Ltd
United Kingdom

www.piperbooks.co.uk
enquiries@piperbooks.co.uk

This updated book was designed, formatted and produced by Piper Books Ltd